MW00647310

WITH PROFOUND THANKS

Words cannot express the gratitude I feel to everyone who has contributed to the creation of this book. Above all, I am eternally grateful to my Heavenly Father who, in all honesty, is the One who wrote these blends. I believe that God commissioned me to write these blends because He feels the pain of His children. I am nothing more than a vessel to write His ideas. I thank Him for trusting me with such an important task.

First, I want to thank my family. I am so grateful to Alonto Mangandog, my husband, for all the support and faith, and taking care of our children when it was time for me to write; and my children for inspiring me to create a better world for them to grow up in. I thank my sister-in-law and friend, Tarhata Mangandog, for trusting in me, and my parents for believing that I can do anything I put my mind to. I owe much to my acupuncture professor, Neil Gumenick, who taught me that we are, first and foremost, spiritual beings having a human experience. And I must thank my herbology professor, Z'ev Rosenberg, for teaching me how to construct formulas.

Much gratitude goes to my best friends, Mary Sisti and Genevieve Kim, for always believing in my gifts and talents. Thank you, Norma Strange, for consulting me through the book-writing process. And this book would not have been possible without all my business partners and friends who have explored essential oils with me: Jarie Perry, Debbie Ohls, Sarah and Eric Schmidt, Briana Sabaj, and Evi and Pete Felarca—I thank you. You have made this book richer and more effective.

Thank you, Lisa Hewitt, for your support with editing. You made this process so painless for me. And I thank Kristal Molina for making my book come to life.

And of course I owe many thanks to my mentor and friend, Rod Richardson. Without you, none of this would have been possible. You knew what I was capable of the moment we met. Your faith in me made me believe in myself. Thank you, Rod, for opening my world and always being there when I need you.

ABOUT THE AUTHOR

Desiree Mangandog is an acupuncturist and essential oil expert. She specializes in emotional well-being with the use of essential oils and Chinese Medical principles. Desiree is an author, speaker, intuitive healer and thought leader.

Desiree has a Masters of Science in Traditional Oriental Medicine from the Pacific College of Oriental Medicine in San Diego, CA. She entered Chinese Medical school at the age of 20 because of her fervent desire for natural health. She has 13 years of experience in the field of natural health. Her greatest passion is to educate and empower individuals with tools to achieve extraordinary levels of wellness. Her core philosophy is that most physical imbalances are caused by stagnant emotions and limiting beliefs. The key to wellness is to create smooth flow of energy that is rhythmic and consistent, just like a heartbeat

Underlying her work, you will see her deep love for God. Her faith is the cornerstone of all that she is and all that she creates. Desiree strives to live a surrendered life to our Creator and expends energy on eternal matters. She has a profound mission to reach as many people as God allows to impact them with emotional and spiritual well-being. Her vision is to equip people with tools to create an empowered life. She desires for every individual to live their highest self, their divine design. She envisions a world where each of the billions of people on the planet step into their power and live with authenticity. Every soul is a gift. Every person matters greatly. Everyone has something to contribute that the rest of humanity must experience.

Desiree is married to the love of her life, Alonto. They have two beautiful, energetic young boys. The couple met while salsa dancing. They are avid dancers in salsa and west coast swing. This family thrives on adventure and new experiences. Don't be surprised if you see them in random countries sipping coconuts on the beach.

ABOUT THE ILLUSTRATOR

Kristal Coral Marie Molina (molinamama@gmail.com) is an artist living in San Diego, California, with her husband and their two amazing teenagers. Her art is inspired by her artistic family and her Deaf daughter. She also is a sign language Interperter and supporter of the Deaf community. Incorporating her love of art and essential oils has been a dream come true. Kristal cherishes her family and friendships, dirty chai lattes, belly laughs, and hunting at thrift stores for new art projects. Her hope is for everyone to find their artistic side and live whole heartedly. She creates to share the most beautiful part of her soul.

FOREWORD

by Rod Alan Richardson

Years ago, I received a forceful email asking me to contact Desiree Mangandog who was prepared and ready to engage in essential oils. A two hour phone call followed as we connected, worked out the details and got her oils in the mail and on the way. The next few days, I was emailed again by Desiree and informed that she would still use the oils but that she would be going another direction. Disheartened, but hopeful, I patiently waited. I knew that once passion had been discovered, it would be impossible to stay away!

A few months later, I called and asked Desiree if I could fly to California and have dinner with her and her husband Alonto. She agreed. During our meeting, it was clear that her heart was firmly on essential oils and so our journey restarted. Desiree was familiar with natural wellness as a practitioner and acupuncturist. Essential oils were a perfect match. As time has passed, her gift has become apparent as I watch her talent with oils bless the lives of hundreds and thousands.

Many people live out there existence on Earth; however, periodically I've watched as divine designation sets its hand of ordination on specific people. Desiree Mangandog is one of those people. She is a very gifted person with a spiritually appointed mission to bless the lives of others with essential oils. I'm proud to call her friend and hope that her gift will bless your life as she has blessed mine and that you get to know her through these pages as I have had the privilege of doing. After all... You Are Fabulous!

THE OIL CONNECTION

We have been taught that aromatic use is the best way for essential oils to affect our moods and emotions. I am going to challenge that mainstream view. Yes, aromas perceived by the olfactory sense do affect the brain and mood immediately. I have also found that topical application of the oils on specific acupuncture points and meridians yield an even greater change in mood. Chinese medicine teaches us that each organ has a correlating emotion associated with it. The lungs are associated with sadness, liver with anger, the heart with sadness, spleen with worry and over thinking, and kidneys with fear. Unresolved feelings can become trapped in these organs, as well as the corresponding meridians.

Have you ever heard of someone who weeps while receiving a massage? Often, this is because trapped emotions have been released from the tissues. Have you known someone who has never been the same after a traumatic accident? The shock and fear become trapped in joints, bones and muscles. It must be released in order to experience optimum wellness. With these blends, I provide locations along meridians that yield quick results. The combination of specific oils and targeted organ meridians will create quick emotional shifts. I look forward to hearing how empowered you feel after using these blends.

Another concept I teach is that you will not need to use any oil or blend for extended periods of time. Most of these blends will create change within one to six weeks. Some blends will have an impact within a day. Your emotional/spiritual body will change with consistent use, and you will evolve. And then something else will come up and you will need a different blend to address another layer of thoughts and emotions.

Enjoy this journey of self-discovery and empowerment. My whole purpose in writing this book is to awaken you to your true self. The human community needs you to live out your purpose and step into the highest version of yourself. Love must expand in the world so that people can be free from pain, worry and sorrow.

I appreciate each and every one of you, and pray that you experience permanent healing. And always remember that you are fabulous! God bless.

BLENDING DETAILS

This chapter lays out the basic guidelines for blending these formulas, and proper application methods. Feel free to always use your intuition. My recommendations are just that: recommendations. You know your body better than anyone. If you feel the desire to apply the oils in different locations than suggested, then please go right ahead.

All roller-bottle recipes are crafted for a 5 ml roller-bottle size. If you desire to make a 10 ml size, just double the recipe.

The numbers next to each single essential oil indicate the number of drops. Please add the oils in the order in which the recipe is written. The order does energetically affect the outcome of the blend. Western science may say the chemistry is the same, despite the order of adding oils. But I am concerned with the energetics of the blend, not the physical chemistry.

Please use fractionated coconut oil to fill your blends. It is the most neutral carrier oil for essential oils.

And most importantly, make sure your essential oils are pure and therapeutic-grade.

APPLICATION METHODS

There are two things to consider with application methods: location and frequency.

You may apply these blends in any location you prefer. Below are descriptions of common locations and how they may facilitate the oil's effect. Exercise your intuition as to where to apply your blends. We are all different. One blend may yield great results on the inside of wrists for one person, and the same blend may work better on the back of the neck for someone else.

Some of the blends will have specific instructions on where to apply. These recommendations are based on meridians and acupuncture points that I have found to be the most effective.

Blends may be applied as often as needed. One to five times a day is sufficient.

A few blends are extremely potent and will not require an application of more than once or twice per day, and I do indicate which blends fall in this category.

Please be cautious with citrus oils and sun exposure. Bergamot, Lime, Lemon, Wild Orange and Grapefruit can burn the skin if they are applied topically and exposed to the sun. Apply blends containing citrus to the bottoms of the feet if you know you will be out in the sun.

LOCATIONS OF APPLICATION

1. Inside of elbow creases

This is one of my favorite locations to apply oils for emotional well-being. The lung, pericardium and heart channels run through the elbow crease. When applied here, the oils quickly enter the lungs and the heart. In Chinese medicine, these organs are related to sadness and grief. You'll experience the sensation of your chest opening and feeling lighter when you apply blends to the inside of elbow creases.

2. Inside of wrist creases

The lung, pericardium and heart channels also run through the wrist creases. Essential oils applied here also move quickly to the chest. This is an easy, accessible location to apply oils.

3. Inside forearms

Roll up and down the inside of forearms—both sides—to have oils circulate quickly throughout the body. Many veins are close to the skin on the inside of the forearms, so the oils enter the bloodstream rapidly. This is the best location to instantly create change in your emotional state.

4. Back of neck or spine

Apply blends to the back of your neck or spine when you need mental clarity. It is a quick way for oils to enter the brain.

5. Over the heart area

This location is on the sternum, between the breasts (or nipple line). It is not the literal heart. Apply blends here when dealing with heartache and disappointment.

6. Around the belly button

This is a special place to apply oils. My favorite oils to apply around the belly button are those related to protection and boundaries, and an increase in immune-system function.

7. Up and down midline of the belly

Apply oils here when they're related to self-confidence and self-worth issues. Your belly has many serotonin receptors that contribute to feelings of happiness and self-esteem. The belly is an underutilized location for essential oil application. As when applying to the inside of the forearms, you will feel the shift immediately when applying oils on the belly.

8. Bottoms of feet

This is one of the most popular locations to apply oils. This is the preferred location when you need calmness and grounding.

9. Inhale from the hands

Sometimes you just want to inhale the oil. One inhale sends the aromatic compounds to the brain and shifts your entire chemistry. Every blend can be used through inhaling alone.

Blends for Inspiration

DROPS

8 Bergamot	2 Rosemary	1 Black Pepper
3 Coriander	3 Frankincense	1 Clove
2 Clary Sage	1 Cinnamon	2 Wild Orange
	1 Spearmint	
	1 Vetiver	

Place drops in a 5ml roller bottle. Fill the rest with fractionated coconut oil. Apply to inside of wrist creases, back of neck, and over heart area.

Be Yourself

Be Yourself is used when a person is on a journey of self-discovery. The noise of society, family expectations, and what media teaches often are in conflict with your true nature. This blend guides you to be true to yourself, and never let another person define who you are and what you are capable of. We are limitless beings with abounding creative energy. Our role is to focus that energy into the projects we are meant to bring to fruition.

Another dilemma in our modern world is too many choices. A wise soul knows what he or she is meant to be doing in the present moment and responds with action. Allow the Be Yourself blend to guide you back to you. It will help you honor the magnificent being you are, and keep you honest with yourself. This is ultimate self-acceptance. All the answers you seek can be found within you.

BLEND BREAKDOWN

Bergamot helps you to fall in love with yourself! It is the oil that teaches unconditional self-acceptance. Bergamot eliminates negative self-criticism that stops you from moving forward.

Coriander is the oil of honesty. Most people are in denial of their passions and dreams, in the effort to be "practical" and pay the bills. Coriander will lead you to be honest with yourself and demand more out of life than just making a living.

Clary Sage opens your spiritual vision to see your truth. When you become intimate with your spirit, you will begin to genuinely understand who you are and the power that resides within. This will blow your mind.

Rosemary expands your perception of reality and guides you to look deep within. It also helps with the transition of higher self-awareness.

Frankincense obliterates darkness and brings the truth to light.

Cinnamon ignites passion and enthusiasm for living your purpose.

Spearmint instills confidence and brings clarity to your truth.

Vetiver grounds you in all this newfound love and appreciation for yourself.

Black Pepper pulls off all of the fake masks you have put on to pretend you are happy and have your life together.

Clove instills power and conviction of your truth.

Wild Orange brings gladness to the heart and joy for your journey.

5 Douglas Fir

8 Patchouli

3 Clary Sage

5 Eucalyptus

3 Rosemary

5 Wintergreen

2 Sandalwood (Indian or Hawaiian)

1 Cinnamon

1 Lemon

Place drops in a 5 ml roller bottle. Fill the rest with fractionated coconut oil. Apply to the temples and back of neck. Be careful not to get this blend in your eyes.

Mend the Heart

Mend the Heart is for the brokenhearted. At times, loved ones betray our trust or make choices that disappoint. Using this blend will help heal the damage and mend the wounded heart. It may also help restore trust in people and give hope for those who have wronged us. *Mend the Heart* will prevent you from falling into bitterness, resentment and grudges against those who created the pain. Often, betrayals cause you to form a wall to prevent others from fully entering into your heart. This blend should be used immediately after hearing the shock of a betrayal/disappointment.

BLEND BREAKDOWN

Ylang Ylang is a significant heart-nourishing oil. Pain might create energetic holes in the heart. Ylang Ylang rushes straight to the heart and fills those holes. Hence, this oil restores the childlike innocence and joy we all once experienced.

Helichrysum is known as "liquid stitches." Where Ylang Ylang fills up the holes, Helichrysum acts like the stitches that hold the emotional "tissues" together until the heart fully heals. Within a month the heart should be fully restored and the emotional tissues fused back together.

Juniper Berry allows you to truly feel the pain of betrayal in order to release it. Mend the Heart is not about ignoring the pain and forcing it to quickly go away. Most individuals ignore pain and stuff it down (often using addictions as a salve) for years. This brings ongoing unwellness. To facilitate healing, it is important to embrace and fully feel the pain—endure the ugly cry, so that you become stronger and move on, feeling restored.

Wild Orange brings brightness to the heart.

Myrrh nourishes the heart, reminding you that everything is going to be OK. It helps you to remember that you have all the love and support you need to make it through.

Douglas Fir brightens the mind and increases wisdom. This oil helps you to grow and become wiser through painful events.

Spearmint helps you verbally express the pain to people who love you unconditionally. Lack of verbal expression can cause your health to deteriorate, so it is vital to speak your truth.

Place in a 5ml roller bottle. Fill the rest with fractionated coconut oil. Apply to inside of elbow creases, chest and the midline of the belly.

DROPS
10 Cedarwood
4 Cassia
4 Wintergreen
2 Clary Sage
6 Siberian Fir

Soothe the Soul

Soothe the Soul is used when your spirit is exhausted and has endured severe hardship. This blend is appropriate for circumstances such as leaving a job, enduring difficulty in close relationships, facing legal battles, moving, or working on challenging projects/tests at school or work. It will give you the strength to cross the finish line with grace and ease.

Soothe the Soul is used any time you need to take a deep breath and let out a big sigh. A positive side effect is better breathing patterns. Most individuals do not know how to breathe properly. Cedarwood and Siberian Fir are excellent oils to strengthen the lungs and assist in deeper diaphragmatic breadths.

This blend is also great for those who are chronically stressed about something. Regular use of Soothe the Soul will provide a deep sense of peace and calm.

BLEND BREAKDOWN

Cedarwood is a grounding oil that calms the nerves and nourishes the lungs. It helps you to take deeper breadths and calms anxieties. In Chinese Medicine, lungs are associated with grieving and sadness. Cedarwood addresses loss and disappointment that are buried in the lungs.

Cassia brings comfort to the heart, reminding you that everything will be OK.

Wintergreen detaches you from all the hardship you've endured. You'll be able to step outside yourself and see the struggles from a different perspective. Instead, you'll see it as a growth process and experience gratitude for the difficulties.

Clary Sage provides a "bigger picture" of your situation, which helps you to understand the importance of challenging moments. Growth of character happens in the trying times.

Siberian Fir helps you let go of burdens that do not belong to you.

Place drops in a 5 ml roller bottle. Fill the rest with fractionated coconut oil. Apply to heart area on sternum, inside of wrists and/or inside of elbow creases. Another great way to apply is up and down the inside of forearms.

DROPS

4 Cinnamon

6 Tangerine

4 Eucalyptus

2 Cassia

3 Lemon

4 Cardamom

Warm Embrace

Warm Embrace is the best blend when you need a big warm hug! Sometimes life feels overwhelming and you just need a shoulder to cry on. This blend is that shoulder and a hug all rolled up in one. When it's applied, you might experience a huge sigh of relief. It makes you feel like everything is going to be more than OK. So if your spouse or a friend isn't available to confide in, bring out *Warm Embrace* to remind you that you are not alone. In fact, you are deeply loved and supported.

BLEND BREAKDOWN

Cinnamon helps you realize how beautiful you are. It is an empowering oil. Cinnamon also releases pain from rejection.

Tangerine brings excitement and joy to the heart. It's easy to get overwhelmed by day-to-day responsibilities. Tangerine helps you to release that pressure and enjoy the current moment.

Eucalyptus reminds you that you can choose to feel healthy and happy at any moment. Your thoughts and emotions are a choice. We all must take responsibility for how we feel. Eucalyptus creates in you the desire to be healthy and feel whole.

Cassia brings warmth and love to the heart. It also reassures you that you are deeply loved.

Lemon cleanses out negative feelings and brings confidence to the spirit.

Cardamom fulfills a unique purpose. It is a great oil for digestion. However, in this blend it is used to help you emotionally "digest" this new way of being/feeling: loved, supported, confident and whole.

Place drops in a 5 ml roller bottle. Fill the rest with fractionated coconut oil.
Apply over heart area three times a day. You also can apply to inside of your wrists.

DROPS

12 Grapefruit

8 Eucalyptus

5 Coriander

3 Ginger

2 Cinnamon

1 Lemon

1 Lavender

1 Spearmint

I Love Myself

I Love Myself is used when you have low self-esteem and have feelings of worthlessness. This blend will help you begin to feel valuable and cherished. You matter. You are created with love and here for a reason. Daily application of I Love Myself will increase your self-confidence. You will also start to take steps in self-care. This includes proper rest, time for meditation, eating healthy, moving your body, pampering activities like pedicures, and anything that shows you are loving yourself. It is the little things that matter. You may not do everything listed, but you will begin to do some of them as you use this blend.

BLEND BREAKDOWN

Grapefruit helps you to prioritize personal needs—especially those regarding better health and personal growth.

Eucalyptus also encourages you to schedule personal care on a daily basis. This oil creates a desire to get healthy emotionally, physically and spiritually.

Coriander helps you to be honest with yourself. It helps you to identify your specific needs. Everyone has different things that nourish the heart. For some, it's reading a book; for others, it's taking a bath. (I personally love massages and writing.)

Ginger strengthens your spirit to take charge of your life. Most women in Western society tend to take care of everyone else and never even put themselves on the list! And men aren't exempt, either. Ginger will change that. It will help you to see how important you are, and how you must put yourself first on the list.

Cinnamon helps you step into your power. You will claim your brilliant beauty, and see yourself as extremely valuable.

Lemon is a purifying oil. It will dispel the internal, negative self-talk that often brings us down.

Lavender helps you to clearly communicate your needs.

Spearmint inspires you to stand strong in yourself and never let anyone make you feel worthless.

35

Place drops in a 5 ml roller bottle. Fill the rest with fractionated coconut oil. Apply to inside of wrists, behind ears, and over the heart.

DROPS

8 Lavender

8 Bergamot

3 Clary Sage

2 Wintergreen

3 Ylang Ylang

2 Spearmint

1 Juniper Berry

1 Helichrysum

2 Frankincense

Say I'm Beautiful

Say I'm Beautiful is a blend for women. It makes you feel beautiful and confident. This blend causes you to ooze self-confidence while communicating with people. Others will listen and be in awe of your beauty. When they smell it on you, it will be difficult for them to pass judgment. Others will only see the beauty of your soul, your mind, your heart and your entire being. A great portion of this blend focuses on increasing your self-confidence and self-esteem. When a woman knows who she is and is proud of who she has become, people can't help but say she is oh, so beautiful.

Psst! Wives, this great blend may influence your husband to say you are beautiful! I used to not hear it enough from my husband, but when I wear this blend he says it every time!

BLEND BREAKDOWN

Lavender assists in easy expression of your true self. It helps you to be authentic, which is the ultimate form of beauty. People love authenticity.

Bergamot helps you accept yourself for who you are and increase your confidence. When you own your confidence, it is very attractive to others.

Clary Sage changes how you perceive yourself, especially if you struggle with negative self-talk. This oil opens your eyes to see your own beauty.

Wintergreen encourages you to let go of any negativity you feel about yourself.

Ylang Ylang heals the heart of past pain. This is excellent if you were ridiculed, made fun of during childhood or adulthood, or looked down upon. Ylang Ylang will melt away that pain for good, so that true joy can be experienced.

Spearmint increases confidence and the ability to express yourself with tremendous impact. The words will fly out of your mouth like a sonnet. Spearmint and Lavender is an excellent combination to apply on the throat when speaking for a living or connecting with many people.

Juniper Berry will release any fears or hesitation that block you from expressing your true self.

Helichrysum is another important oil to heal the pain from low self-esteem.

Frankincense reveals the truth of how precious and magnificent you are, because we are wonderfully and fearfully made.

Place drops in a 5 ml roller bottle. Fill the rest with fractionated coconut oil. Apply the blend on the chest, back of neck and inside of the elbow creases.

DROPS

12 Bergamot

2 Cassia

3 Peppermint

3 Ginger

3 Spearmint

8 Cedarwood

1 Cinnamon

2 Ylang Ylang

1 Lavender

1 Marjoram

Be Brave

Be Brave is used when you know it is time to make a significant change in your life. It's ideal to use when the change is drastic, and many fears come up because you believe making the jump is a huge risk. This blend will help you to be bold and courageous—to take that leap of faith, despite what naysayers tell you. Have you ever had a strong desire to do something or go somewhere, but you've convinced yourself that it's impossible? Maybe you are afraid that this desire is irresponsible or impractical, but deep down inside your soul is crying out to take the plunge and follow your dreams. Let your heart sing and be brave in your choices.

BLEND BREAKDOWN

Bergamot teaches you to completely love and accept yourself, and provides an optimistic view of your journey.

Cassia encourages you to put yourself out there no matter what others think.

Peppermint teaches us that the past does not equal our future. We can create any outcome we desire.

Ginger makes you feel that you can accomplish whatever your heart desires. Nothing will stop you from creating your dreams.

Spearmint frees you of inhibitions and inspires you to be bold.

Cedarwood grounds in this newfound bravery, so that it becomes your new normal. Gone are the days of being quiet and holding back.

Cinnamon enhances the attractive parts of your personality.

Ylang Ylang brings excitement to the heart as you embark on a new path. You'll start to feel the butterflies.

Lavender allows other to accept and hear what you are telling them.

Marjoram opens the heart so that you allow the right people into your life. People come into our lives at specific times to guide us. You must be open to let them into your space to help you grow.

8 Cedarwood

5 Cassia

5 Wild Orange

3 Grapefruit

3 Marjoram

2 Ylang Ylang

Place drops in a 5 ml roller bottle. Fill the rest with fractionated coconut oil. Apply over the heart, inside of wrists, and back of neck.

Connected

Connected reminds you that you are not alone. Everyone is part of the greater human community, and also a part of smaller communities. This blend is especially for those who are afraid to create intimate bonds with others. It takes vulnerability to connect with another person, and sometimes it's scary to open our hearts wide. However, true love and joy are experienced in that vulnerability.

You may benefit from this blend if you were hurt in the past, and then decided to create a wall and not let anyone get close to your heart. It's a defense mechanism. However, if that wall is up all the time, then love can't enter in, either.

Connected will help you begin letting others deeply in, and also remind you that you are safe. This blend also may provide discernment on who is safe to let in, and who is not.

BLEND BREAKDOWN

Cedarwood helps you recognize that many people love and support you.

Cassia provides self-confidence and helps you see your true beauty.

Wild Orange allows you to feel the warmth and love in your heart from all the people connected to you.

Grapefruit gives you discernment on who to let in and who to keep out of your space.

Marjoram breaks down the walls that block the heart from opening, and restores trust in humanity.

Ylang Ylang heals the heart from past pain and heartache. This oil also helps to restore your faith in people. There are many kind, loving people in the world. Ylang Ylang will create the desire to deeply connect with those exceptional people we meet daily.

Blends for the Mind

DROPS

5 Basil

8 Grapefruit

10 Lavender

3 Thyme

1 Wintergreen

Place drops in a 5 ml roller bottle. Fill the rest with fractionated coconut oil. Apply to the temples and back of neck. Be careful not to get this blend in your eyes.

Decisions, Decisions

Decisions, Decisions is a blend that helps an individual with small or large decisions. The person who benefits the most from this blend is one who has the most difficult time making any kind of decision: for example, when you go to a restaurant, look at the menu, and are completely paralyzed because you can't decide which item to choose.

Another great time to use this blend is when you have come to a fork in the road and have to make a significant decision that will alter the course of your life.

BLEND BREAKDOWN

Basil is excellent for the overwhelming kind of stress that leads to indecision.

Grapefruit guides you to make the best decisions that are nourishing to the body, mind and spirit.

Lavender allows you to express your needs to others. It will help you to access inner thoughts and desires that have never been expressed. When uncovering these things, lavender will aid you in making the best decisions for you.

Thyme brings up suppressed emotions to the surface. Ignoring these emotions can cloud judgment. By uncovering those emotions that have been buried, more clarity will emerge and decision-making will be effortless.

Wintergreen helps you let go of everything needing to be perfect. Perfectionism can cause a paralyzing fear of making the wrong choice, resulting in what is known as "analysis paralysis"—taking no action. This oil will help you to make a decision, even if it isn't perfect. Course correction can be made anytime, but it requires forward movement. The journey begins with making a decision.

Collected is for those of us who spread our attention in a million different directions. You may be easily distracted and over committed—the mom (or dad) who says "yes" to everything and everyone, even when she would rather not. This means she's always on the go and never takes time for herself. *Collected* will help this over committed type to slow down and make self-care a priority.

A very grounding blend, *Collected* will help you to allow yourself to accept divine grace. It also helps to raise the awareness that you are not alone doing everything; you have God, who is the source of all power and energy. If you're using divine energy, you should not be exhausted all the time. Exhaustion is a sign that something is off balance.

Place drops in a 5 ml roller bottle. Fill the rest with fractionated coconut oil. Apply to back of neck, behind ears and inside of wrists. You can apply this blend up to five times per day.

DROPS

8 Arborvitae

9 Lemon

5 Myrrh

3 Patchouli

5 Cedarwood

2 Clary Sage

1 Coriander

1 Siberian Fir

1 Vetiver

1 Grapefruit

1 Frankincense

Collected

BLEND BREAKDOWN

Arborvitae helps you to trust that God is the one leading the details of our lives, and we are not alone in taking care of everything. When we realize that God is in control and has everything handled, this can bring us to a deep sense of peace.

Lemon cleanses the soul of low vibration. The idea that you have to take care of life's demands all by yourself is most definitely a low vibration. Lemon also can bring joy to the heart, clear the mind, and give you the gift of living in the present moment.

Myrrh is a nourishing oil for the heart. This is best for those who have difficulty trusting others because of a previous betrayal or disappointment. Myrrh helps begin to open the heart and bring people back into our lives.

Patchouli helps to ground the spirit into the body. Often you may be easily distracted because there is a disconnect between the body and the spirit. Patchouli helps to integrate the body and spirit, and helps you learn to operate with them in unison.

Cedarwood is another grounding oil. Its main purpose is to help you recognize that you are a part of a larger community, and that this community desires to support you in your journey. No one is an island. Your divine life purposes require a loving community surrounding you for encouragement and support.

Clary Sage provides a bigger picture of what is going on. It opens the mind's eye to the truth. This will open you to new ideas and allow for a major paradigm shift. Making the change from always saying "yes," to saying "no" and asking for help, requires an enormous shift in mindset. Clary Sage can assist in this transition by helping you to see the importance of allowing people to help.

Coriander encourages you to honor yourself and do what is right.

Siberian Fir helps break patterns of doing it all without any help. In Western culture, this behavior pattern is an epidemic, especially for women. Women are expected to have successful careers, be the perfect mom, cook every single meal, keep the house perfectly clean, and make sure the kids are involved in many sports/activities. This is a lot of pressure on one person, and it is not sustainable.

Vetiver allows you to become more rooted. This will dispel feelings of being "scattered."

Grapefruit teaches you to respect your body by giving it what it needs. This may mean taking a nap, exercising, getting a massage, or anything that nourishes your body and soul. And it gently teaches you that you deserve to take care of yourself without any feelings of guilt.

Frankincense is used in the blend to enhance and harmonize the entire formula. Another great function of Frankincense is to help protect from negative influences.

DROPS

8 Fennel

8 Clary Sage

5 Cedarwood

3 Thyme

2 Ylang Ylang

1 Lime

1 Arborvitae

1 Frankincense

Place drops in a 5 ml roller bottle. Fill the rest with fractionated coconut oil. Apply to inside of elbow creases and around the belly button.

Responsibilities

Responsibilities. Sometimes the word conjures up negative, heavy emotions. This blend is for you if you feel overburdened by the weight of all your responsibilities. I know all too well the crushing feeling and self-disappointment when not taking care of all my "responsibilities."

If you are ready to be free from that heaviness, then use this blend! It will give you greater perspective on what you actually are responsible for and what you are not. My guess is that you've created a longer list of responsibilities than you should. It's time to learn to delegate and ask for help. In our Western society, often women take on too much! There is this expectation of having to be the perfect mom, cook every single meal, have the ideal career, keep the house perfectly tidy, home school the kids, stay in shape, be the perfect wife, and be perfect at everything!! And get eight hours of sleep every night. This blend will definitely breakdown that ridiculous view.

BLEND BREAKDOWN

Fennel will bring awareness to what your actual responsibilities are.

Clary Sage will open your mind to a new way of viewing your life.

Cedarwood encourages you to reach out to your community and receive support from others.

Thyme releases the frustration associated with having so much to do.

Ylang Ylang brings back the childlike joy and wonder we all once had. This helps you to live in the present moment and appreciate all the blessings in your life.

Lime is another great oil for cleansing frustration.

Arborvitae helps to release that controlling nature of, "This is how it has to be done." This oil brings grace and flow to the spirit, so that you experience peace. It's a great oil for letting go of the need to be right.

Frankincense heightens feelings of peace and serenity. It's a great enhancing oil to Arborvitae. You can joyfully take care of your responsibilities and be grateful for them.

DROPS

8 Melaleuca

5 Lemongrass

3 Oregano

2 Lemon

2 Lavender

1 Wild Orange

1 Eucalyptus

1 Peppermint

1 Siberian Fir

1 Douglas Fir

Place drops in a 5 ml roller bottle. Fill the rest with fractionated coconut oil. Apply to the back of neck, temples, and inside of elbow creases.

Still My Mind

Still My Mind is an ideal blend for you if your mind is constantly running and you can't seem to shut it off. Often, the same thoughts will churn inside one's head—the same worries and concerns. This blend will help eliminate the thoughts that don't serve you. It is very specific to eliminate fear-based, negative self-talk. At the same time, *Still My Mind* will enhance encouraging self-talk that will help lead to growth and empowerment. It is a purifying blend that cleanses out self-limiting beliefs.

This blend is also great to use before meditation. It helps you to be present, quiet and calm.

BLEND BREAKDOWN

Melaleuca is an energetically disinfecting oil. It is great at clearing out any negative vibrations in your head.

Lemongrass cleanses out limiting beliefs. It's one of the best oils to use when there is a lot of negativity to release—for example, things or people who bring you down, or circumstances not meant to be a part of your life.

Oregano powerfully severs ties with energetic baggage. Sometimes the constant thinking comes from being involved with people, things, or organizations that are toxic to your spirit.

Lemon is a key purification oil that cleanses out negative beliefs. It refreshes and uplifts the spirit.

Lavender helps you communicate to others your new way of thinking, since this blend will evaporate all the limiting beliefs that previously held you back.

Wild Orange is an encouraging oil that brings beautiful things into your world.

Peppermint, Siberian Fir and **Douglas Fir** help to invigorate the lungs and circulate the formula quickly throughout the body system.

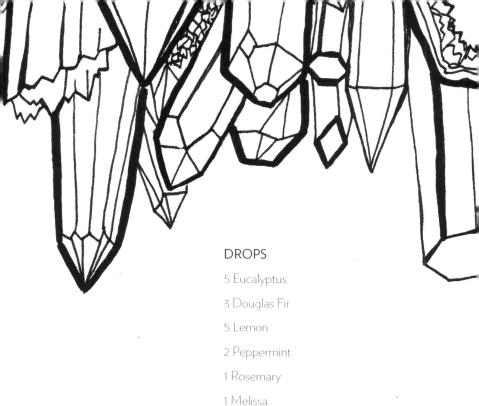

DROPS

5 Eucalyptus

3 Douglas Fir

5 Lemon

2 Peppermint

1 Rosemary

1 Melissa

1 Wintergreen

3 Lemongrass

1 Cardamom

Place drops in a 5 ml roller bottle. Fill the rest with fractionated coconut oil. Apply to back of neck, temples, and inside of elbow creases.

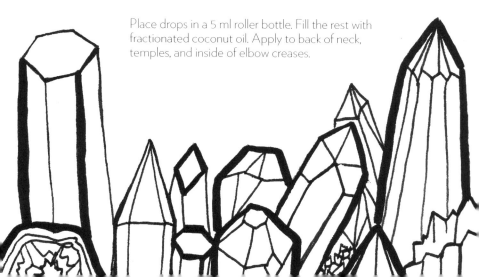

Clarity

Clarity is an excellent blend for those who struggle with constant confusion, especially those who experience "foggy brain." Some describe it as a dark cloud in and around the head. The oils in *Clarity* open up the mind and get rid of the muck that creates low energy. You will be able to hear yourself think, be very present when communicating with others, and radiate vibrant energy.

BLEND BREAKDOWN

Eucalyptus and **Douglas Fir** both powerfully opens up the brain and create massive energy flow. In Chinese medicine the foggy brain is referred to as "hidden phlegm" in the mind. These oils assist in breaking through the hidden phlegm. This isn't literal phlegm—it is a thick, sticky energy.

Lemon also breaks down hidden phlegm. It is responsible for clearing the mind of negative thoughts and bringing positive ideas to the surface.

Peppermint is another head-opening/clearing oil. It creates movement of energy. Peppermint also resolves feelings of frustration and irritability associated with "foggy-headedness."

Rosemary assists in the transition of confusion to clarity. Sometimes it can be difficult to believe that your life can change for the better. Rosemary brings confidence that it is possible to improve your current situation.

Melissa shows you how brilliant and beautiful you are. It is difficult to have low energy when you see how powerful and important you are in this world.

Wintergreen allows you to abandon your worries and fears, and trust in the journey of wellness.

Lemongrass clears destructive thoughts that tear you down. This oil helps you let go of old ways of thinking and embrace the new patterns of empowering beliefs.

Cardamom provides perspective on why you have been unclear. Awareness alone can create positive change. That understanding will prevent you from returning to old patterns that no longer serve you.

Abundance
Blends

DROPS

5 Eucalyptus

3 Rosemary

5 Myrrh

3 Siberian Fir

3 Frankincense

2 Cypress

1 Lemon

Place drops in a 5 ml roller bottle. Fill the rest with fractionated coconut oil. Apply to inside of elbow crease, chest and back of neck.

More Money Blend

The **More Money Blend** is used when you literally feel it's time to increase money in your life. This blend is philosophically deeper than it seems. It takes a certain way of being to attract more money into your life. There must be openness and willingness to receive blessings. Most individuals struggle with feeling undeserving/unworthy of receiving wealth, and live in a space of scarcity. The **More Money Blend** helps to rewire how you feel about abundance and allows that abundance to flow freely into your life.

BLEND BREAKDOWN

Eucalyptus is the best oil to use when you are stuck in scarcity mindset. It creates the desire to expand and recognize that you must take ownership of your circumstances. If you can create scarcity, you can surely create abundance.

Rosemary is critical to use when shifting your paradigm. It is quite a jump from the "scarcity" way of being to living in abundant thinking.

Myrrh provides feelings of safety and comfort amid great change. It soothes the soul and reminds you that you are taken care of completely.

Siberian Fir assists in breaking poor money habits that have been passed down the generations. This oil helps to break patterns such as a lack of putting money in savings, a resistance to investing, a habit of spending more money than you earn, or gambling.

Frankincense shows you the fact that you come from abundance. No human being lacks creativity, innovation and greatness. We come from greatness, and that is what we are to reflect.

Cypress and **Lemon** powerfully moves any stagnant thoughts that block you from receiving wealth.

DROPS

12 Eucalyptus
5 Douglas Fir
5 Marjoram
3 Patchouli
2 Lavender
1 Cinnamon
1 Cypress
1 Arborvitae
3 Lime
1 Ylang Ylang

Place drops in a 5 ml roller bottle. Fill the rest with fractionated coconut oil. Apply over heart area and back of neck. Apply twice a day until momentum has taken over.

Momentum

Momentum is used when you are about to embark on a new journey that requires significant effort to get going. This is comparable to the amount of energy required for a train to leave the station: there is a great push at first, but after awhile the train maintains high speeds with less effort.

Use **Momentum** in situations such as when you're starting a new business or a new project, beginning to take care of your physical health, entering into college, or something similar.

This blend will help you gracefully move into new beginnings and quickly get traction toward success. The side effect is rapid expansion into yourself—meaning your gifts and talents will expand at an astronomical rate. You should use this blend only when you are ready for increased activity and change.

BLEND BREAKDOWN

Eucalyptus uplifts the spirit and increases your physical energy, so you're ready and able to embrace new projects.

Douglas Fir invigorates your mind and helps you see the bigger picture. In a way, it helps you see the light at the end of the tunnel.

Marjoram softens the heart and allows you to trust in the process.

Patchouli connects the heart and the mind. It helps you take your grand ideas and manifest them physically.

Lavender improves communication so that people can clearly understand the vision.

Cinnamon helps you stand in your power.

Cypress powerfully removes stagnations and any blocks. Even though it's one drop in the blend, it is the critical oil that creates great momentum in your life.

Arborvitae brings in divine power to help support and create momentum.

Lime brings excitement to your heart for all the growth and change.

Ylang Ylang brings joy and gratitude to the heart.

Place drops in 5 ml roller bottle. Fill the rest with fractionated coconut oil. Apply to midline of belly, inside of elbow creases, and inside wrist creases.

DROPS
5 Spearmint
5 Wild Orange
3 Lavender
3 Bergamot
3 Tangerine
3 Grapefruit
2 Cinnamon
1 Cypress
1 Helichrysum
2 Lime
1 Frankincense

More than Enough

More than Enough is a blend to bring you to a place of abundance. Most people live from a place of scarcity, and feel there is never enough money, time, talent or creativity. And that space is intensely stressful. It is important to feel that there is more than enough—further, that there is too much abundance and you are overflowing with blessings. We forget that abundance first comes within, and then it manifests outwardly. *More than Enough* will bring feelings of complete satisfaction, peace and a desire to give to others. You will recognize that you already have everything you need and begin to see all the beauty that exists around you.

BLEND BREAKDOWN

Spearmint and **Wild Orange** together clear the mind of scarcity thinking. They instill confidence that there is more than enough for everyone to enjoy.

Lavender brings awareness to your speech. You'll notice the times when you say, "I don't have enough money," or "I don't have enough time." Lavender will help you recognize the thought before you verbalize it. Verbalization is a powerful way to manifest positive or negative outcomes.

Tangerine teaches you how to become resourceful with what is in your reach.

Grapefruit helps you to appreciate who you are and what you are capable of.

Cinnamon opens the heart and brings warmth to the spirit. It guides you to stand in your power.

Cypress moves stagnant energy and shakes things up. Scarcity is a learned pattern, and cypress greatly breaks up that pattern.

Helichrysum heals the emotional trauma that comes with the stress of living in the world of "not enough."

Lime excites the spirit as you enter the world of more than enough.

Frankincense brings to light all your gifts and talents that are meant to be shared with the world.

Place drops in a 5 ml roller bottle. Fill the rest with fractionated coconut oil. Apply to inside of elbow creases, inside of forearms and back of neck. Apply twice a day for a month.

DROPS

5 Cypress
3 Douglas Fir
3 Siberian Fir
2 Wild Orange
2 Myrrh
3 Geranium
3 Coriander
2 Clary Sage
1 Patchouli
1 Hawaiian Sandalwood
1 Ginger
2 Cedarwood

Manifestor's Blend

Manifestor's Blend is for those of you who have many great ideas or glimpses of your highest potential, yet have not manifested them into your life. This blend will help take those ideas and make them real. Many creative people have this dilemma. They can imagine and picture something grand, but struggle to make it happen. Use *Manifestor's Blend* if you are serious about making your dreams into reality.

BLEND BREAKDOWN

Cypress opens up your spirit and creates powerful flow of creative energy. Cypress also reminds you that your past does not equal your future. It will cause you to create a different life from the one you had in the past.

Douglas Fir and **Siberian Fir** both assist in letting go of self-sabotage. Your head will fill with new ideas on how to make your dreams a reality.

Wild Orange reminds you of the ample creative energy that is available to flow through you. Everyone has several beautiful projects waiting to be born.

Myrrh provides feelings of being nurtured during this journey. Changing direction and encouraging your creative output can sometimes cause violent opposition among those who do not support your journey. Myrrh reminds you that despite naysayers, there are more people who love and support you while you are going for your dreams.

Geranium births feelings of trust that you are on the right path.

Coriander guides you to always be true to yourself.

Clary Sage keeps the image of your success right in front of you. This way, you are continually reminded of who you are to become.

Patchouli brings all these ideas and grounds them into the body. This is the most critical oil in making dreams a reality. Once those ideas are grounded into the body, they are easier to manifest.

Hawaiian Sandalwood connects the mind and the heart. It brings those ideas and connects them to how you would feel when reaching your highest self. It is the intense emotion behind the idea that drives a person to act.

Ginger encourages you to create massive action.

Cedarwood harmonizes the blend and circulates it throughout the system.

Place drops in a 5 ml roller bottle. Fill the rest with fractionated coconut oil. Apply over the heart, behind ears and inside of wrists. This blend can be applied up to five times a day.

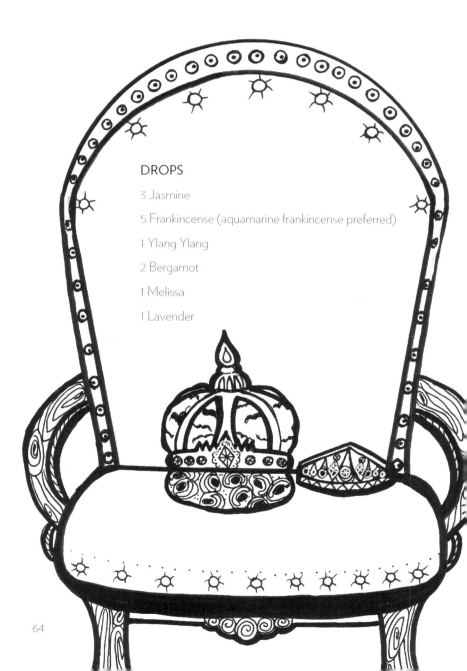

DROPS

3 Jasmine

5 Frankincense (aquamarine frankincense preferred)

1 Ylang Ylang

2 Bergamot

1 Melissa

1 Lavender

Royalty

There is nothing as sweet as feeling like royalty! Everyone has a secret dream of being a prince or princess. I personally believe that every human being is a royal.

Royalty blend will create those feelings of being regal, majestic and supreme. When you use this blend, others will feel your confidence and power. They will want to work with you and engage with you as a friend or in a business relationship. This is a highly attractive oil. People will begin to flock to you in droves and want to be around you. You must be prepared for all this attention when you decide to use the *Royalty* blend.

This is an important blend to use when you struggle with seeing your own beauty and worth. Another possible side effect is that you will step into your divine purpose.

BLEND BREAKDOWN

Jasmine brings out the purest and most beautiful side of you. It helps you to walk with poise, grace and elegance.

Frankincense allows you to reflect your light out to the world. This makes you brilliant and attractive.

Ylang Ylang makes you feel beautiful.

Bergamot strengthens the spirit. It uplifts and enhances your self-confidence.

Melissa magnifies the brilliant beauty within each person.

Lavender improves communication. It will help you speak with eloquence as you voice your truth to the world.

Empowering Blends

DROPS

8 Cinnamon

3 Spearmint

2 Wild Orange

1 Lemon

1 Grapefruit

1 Bergamot

1 Siberian Fir

Place drops in a 5 ml roller bottle. Fill the rest with fractionated coconut oil. Apply to chest, inside of elbow crease, inside of forearms and/or back of neck.

I am Fabulous

I am Fabulous is the signature blend for this book! It brings strong feelings of self-confidence and excitement to the soul. You will feel invincible and believe that you can accomplish anything you put your mind to. *I am Fabulous* also helps you to see how exquisite and powerful you are. Every human being is created with extraordinary talent, and this blend will encourage you to embrace your gifts and share them with the world. This is the ultimate empowering blend, as well as a self-love blend.

BLEND BREAKDOWN

Cinnamon connects you with your inner strength, so you can charge forward, despite any obstacle.

Spearmint causes you to carry yourself with grace and poise, and the ability to convey that confidence to the people around you.

Wild Orange helps you to see the possibilities that surround you, so that you will fearlessly step into your destined path.

Lemon channels your efforts so that you can concentrate on the most important activities that contribute to your life's purpose.

Grapefruit reminds you to take care of yourself physically, mentally and emotionally. It is important to prioritize your self-care every single day. The more you prioritize your needs, the more fabulous you feel!

Bergamot helps you embrace and cherish your fabulous self.

Siberian Fir breaks harmful thought patterns such as "I'm not good enough," "I'm not deserving," or "I'm not smart enough."

5 Frankincense

3 Juniper Berry

2 Spearmint

5 Wild Orange

2 Rosemary

3 Myrrh

1 Lavender

3 Eucalyptus

1 Arborvitae

2 Bergamot

Place drops in a 5 ml roller bottle. Fill the rest with fractionated coconut oil. Apply all over the belly. Roll it up and down until you cover every inch of your belly. Apply three times a day for one week, and then twice a day for four weeks.

I Am Whole

I Am Whole is for those who feel they are broken and not good enough. This blend reminds you that you are already perfect in the eyes of God. You are greatly loved and cherished. It's the delusion that we are empty that creates destructive patterns such as food addiction, drug or alcohol addiction, gambling addiction, excessive gaming, phone addiction and other negative behaviors. In essence, this is a spiritual crisis. *I Am Whole* is the blend of choice to free you from unhealthy obsessive patterns.

BLEND BREAKDOWN

Frankincense helps you see your divine nature.

Juniper Berry releases the fear of not being good enough.

Spearmint instills confidence to help you overcome unhealthy addictions.

Wild Orange helps you taste the sweetness of life, and remind you that there is much to live for.

Rosemary helps with the transition from feeling broken to feeling whole.

Myrrh takes you out of the "flight or fight" mode that leads to constant stress. It is in that space where addictions take hold. Myrrh nourishes the soul and provides feelings of security and safety.

Lavender soothes and calms the spirit.

Eucalyptus creates the desire to shift into healthy habits.

Arborvitae is a peaceful and grounding oil. You will feel calm and rooted. This is important because addictions come from an unsettled spirit, which leads to consumptive energy.

Bergamot builds trust in yourself that you can make this change.

Place drops in a 5 ml roller bottle. Fill the rest with fractionated coconut oil. Apply to throat and inside of wrists.

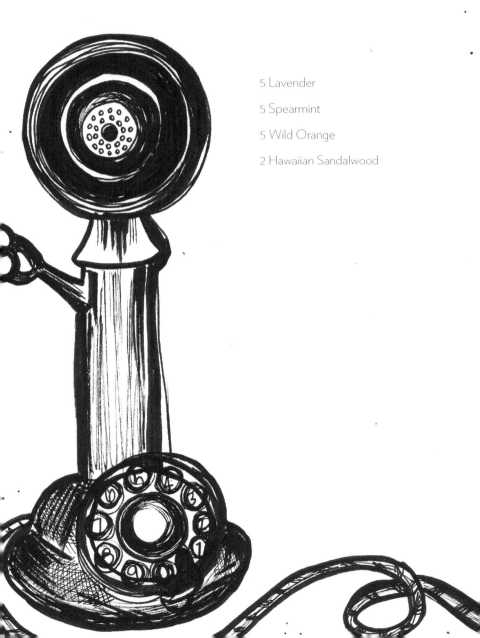

5 Lavender

5 Spearmint

5 Wild Orange

2 Hawaiian Sandalwood

Speaker's Blend

Speaker's Blend is for anyone who speaks for a living. This includes teachers, singers, actors, public speakers, network marketers, customer service representatives, and more. *Speaker's Blend* assists in improved communication skills. It helps you to speak eloquently and get your ideas across effectively. Not only does it improve your speech, it also helps you to listen clearly to the other person's needs. That way when you respond, you will be speaking in their language. You will speak the words they need to hear.

Speaker's Blend will not keep you in your head. It actually may improve your heart-to-heart connection with others, so that you build instant rapport. Watch how this blend enhances your listening skills.

Speaker's Blend may also be used for those who have a difficult time expressing themselves. You don't necessarily have to speak for a living to use this blend.

BLEND BREAKDOWN

Lavender helps you find the words that need to be said. This is the greatest oil for self-expression. Lavender does bring about emotional maturity because you will express your truth to others.

Spearmint allows you to speak with boldness. Your words will penetrate the hearts of listeners, and they will respect what you have to say.

Wild Orange creates an eagerness to share yourself with others.

Hawaiian Sandalwood creates an intimate bond with every person you interact with. It helps you feel one with another, and even one with an audience. This is possible because Hawaiian Sandalwood deepens heart-to-heart connection.

Place drops in a 5 ml roller bottle. Fill the rest with fractionated coconut oil. Apply around the belly button and then up the midline of belly. Apply once in the morning after waking and once at night before bed for 6 weeks. Further application is not necessary, as you will have learned the pattern of creating healthy boundaries.

DROPS

8 Clove

12 Melaleuca

5 Marjoram

3 Cedarwood

2 Cinnamon

1 Lime

Boundaries

Boundaries helps you to set clear and definite boundaries with others. This blend is excellent if you believe you're a pushover who says "yes" to everything and has a hard time saying "no." Some commitments, we are meant to say "yes" to, but there are more activities we are meant to say "no" to.

Most people who have difficulty saying no are those who care deeply about the opinions of others. But remember, the opinions of others do not define who you are. **Boundaries** also helps protect you from letting in people who may not have the best intentions—for example, those who take advantage, steal energy, dump their problems, lie, and have wicked hearts. This blend—by default—helps enhance the love and beauty between friends and family that have the best intentions for us.

BLEND BREAKDOWN

Clove is an empowering oil that encourages you to stand up for yourself. It reminds you that you have the power to take charge of your life, and have a right to set high standards.

Melaleuca creates boundaries that allow for healthy relationship to enter your space, and keeps out dysfunctional relationships.

Marjoram helps you to open your heart and be vulnerable with people who genuinely love and support you. It also will guide you to protect your heart against individuals who intend to take advantage of you. Marjoram provides discernment so that you know who to and who not to allow in your space.

Cedarwood provides comfort to the soul that you are safe and protected.

Cinnamon dispels fears and helps you feel powerful. You will feel confident that no one can harm you.

Lime helps to circulate the blend throughout the body. In Chinese Medicine, we often use certain herbs as envoys to spread the blend to all organs and meridians.

Feel Good
Blends

DROPS

8 Ylang Ylang

5 Patchouli

3 Clary Sage

5 Frankincense

3 Cinnamon

2 Peppermint

1 Cypress

1 Lime

1 Bergamot

Place drops in a 5 ml roller bottle. Fill the rest with fractionated coconut oil. Apply inside of wrists and elbow creases, around belly button, and/or chest.

Fairytale

Welcome to a Fairytale world! This blend will make life feel magical and mystical. You will feel euphoric when applying this blend. People begin to see the magic that life is, and miracles will become an everyday occurrence. Life is beautiful and worries will be no more. This is by far one of my favorite smelling blends. You'll feel the magic the moment you apply it.

BLEND BREAKDOWN

Ylang Ylang brings you back to a childlike state of wonder and awe. When you were little, wasn't the entire world exciting, full of new adventures? You can experience this as an adult, too!

Patchouli brings all this magic into the physical body. It is a very grounding, rooting oil. It integrates the spirit and the body, which contributes to feelings of euphoria.

Clary Sage brings excitement to experiencing the spirit realm. In your mind's eye, you might begin seeing fairies, angels and unicorns!

Frankincense lifts the spirit to a higher level. To see and feel the magic of life, there cannot be any low vibrations. Frankincense helps dispel the low vibrations.

Cinnamon brings passion and excitement.

Peppermint brings the joy of being alive.

Cypress brings fluidity and movement, and welcomes the abundance of divine grace into your heart.

Lime brings feelings of gratitude for everything and everyone you come into contact with.

Bergamot inspires you to be authentic and share your true self with the world.

Place drops in a 5 ml roller bottle. Fill the rest with fractionated coconut oil. Apply to inside of elbow creases and over the chest.

DROPS

8 Coriander	5 Lavender
5 Cardamom	3 Wild Orange
3 Bergamot	2 Cassia
2 Arborvitae	1 Patchouli
3 Marjoram	

Lucky

Lucky is used when it's time for your luck to change. Often we hear that when it rains, it pours. Life can have one series of difficult events after another. If you are ready to allow abundance to flow and uplifting events to occur every day, then Lucky is your blend! The construction of this blend is quite unique. It helps you to be authentic and live your true purpose. It's in our authenticity where abundance flows. Even though the title is **Lucky**, it isn't actual luck that changes the circumstances that occur in our lives. It's a way of being that attracts abundance. And being our true selves attracts positive people and events.

BLEND BREAKDOWN

Coriander helps you to be honest with yourself rather than being in denial. This oil also encourages you to live your authentic self.

Cardamom provides a bigger perspective to see your truth amidst the chaos.

Bergamot brings feelings of luck and excitement. It will make you feel that anything is possible.

Arborvitae helps you to trust that good things can come into your life.

Marjoram increases trust in humanity. There are people out there who genuinely care and will support you in your successes.

Lavender helps to increase your communication of abundant flow with the people around you.

Wild Orange is the key oil in this blend that brings feelings of abundance. There is more than enough out there for you and for everyone else as well.

Cassia helps you see your own magnificence and power.

Patchouli helps ground all of these abundant feelings into the physical body. When they are integrated into the body, then it is easy to manifest great people and circumstances.

Place drops in a 5 ml roller bottle. Fill the rest with fractionated coconut oil. Apply over heart area, inside of elbow creases and back of neck.

8 Lime
3 Lemongrass
5 Marjoram
3 Arborvitae
3 Bergamot
1 Wintergreen
2 Wild Orange
1 Ylang Ylang
1 Siberian Fir
1 Frankincense
1 Eucalyptus

Hop, Skip and a Jump

Are you ready to feel that life is as easy as a *Hop, Skip and a Jump*? I always say that there is only so much difficulty one person can handle. The pendulum eventually has to swing the other way.

This blend is for you if you are ready to feel the excitement of living and magically see life going the way you always dreamed it to. No one grows up with the desire to live a difficult life filled with despair and unending struggles. As kids we dreamed of a glamorous life, changing the world and making a difference. Use Hop, Skip and a Jump and see your luck change. It's time for life to be in your favor. When your attitude is bright and shiny, then love and greatness will be oh, so attracted to you!

BLEND BREAKDOWN

Lime is the ultimate gratitude oil. You will begin to appreciate even the little things, such as the ability to breathe and walk.

Lemongrass cleanses out low vibrations such as despair and feelings of not being good enough.

Marjoram can help you to create close, intimate bonds with others. People are drawn to those whose heart is open.

Arborvitae helps you to be in the flow of life.

Bergamot melts away all the heavy burdens.

Wintergreen inspires you to let go of micromanaging every detail. The universe tends to have ideas that are way bigger than our own.

Wild Orange and Ylang Ylang bring joy to the heart.

Siberian Fir, Frankincense and **Eucalyptus** show the truth of how effortless life can be. When we live in the flow, everything comes easy.

Live In The Present

Place drops in a 5 ml roller bottle. Fill the rest with fractionated coconut oil. Apply to inside of wrists, back of neck, and over the heart.

DROPS

3 Arborvitae

5 Patchouli

5 Clary Sage

2 Geranium

3 Coriander

3 Eucalyptus

2 Rosemary

2 Siberian Fir

2 Vetiver

1 Frankincense

Here and Now

Here and Now is used for those who struggle with living in the present moment. It's common in our modern society to be hyper-focused on future events, worrying about future events, and reminiscing the regrets of our past. Rarely are people fully present in the current moment. Their minds wander elsewhere.

This blend is excellent for the chronic worrywart. *Here and Now* brings you into your body and helps you to focus at the task at hand. This blend will also result in a greater appreciation of the people in your life and all the blessings you are given. A nice side effect of using *Here and Now* is enjoying feelings of extreme gratitude.

BLEND BREAKDOWN

Arborvitae helps one to surrender and let go to the divine plan. Often when we become obsessive about the way things should be, it creates unnecessary hardship and stress.

Patchouli helps to ground the spirit into the body. Chronic worriers are up in their heads and become disconnected with the body. Being grounded is an important aspect of living in the present moment.

Clary Sage provides a greater perspective to the events of your life. Rather than judging a circumstance as being "bad," instead you can look at it as necessary for growth. If anything, Clary Sage will bring up feelings of gratitude for all circumstances that are part of your life journey.

Geranium guides us to trust in the journey.

Coriander brings out your true nature and encourages you to live with authenticity.

Eucalyptus and **Rosemary** both aid in times of major life changes, so that you move into the changes gracefully.

Siberian Fir breaks destructive patterns.

Vetiver is the key oil for grounding and increasing focus.

Frankincense nurtures the spirit, so that you feel loved and protected.

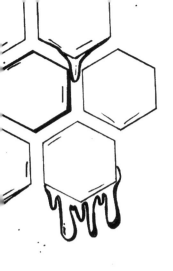

DROPS

3 Rosemary

5 Geranium

3 Pink Wintergreen

2 Thyme

3 Juniper Berry

3 Myrrh

2 Helichrysum

2 Indian Sandalwood

1 Ylang Ylang

Place drops in a 5 ml roller bottle. Fill the rest with fractionated coconut oil. Apply to back of neck, midline of belly and inside of elbow crease.

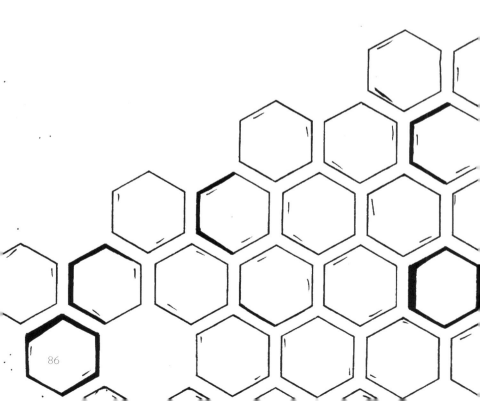

In the Flow

In the Flow is for when you feel you are constantly fighting against life. Things don't seem to go your way and frustration is your predominant emotion. This blend will allow you to be present and move with the natural flow of life. It is a practice of surrender and trust. You'll notice yourself feeling at peace in situations where you normally would be unhinged and stressed. This blend enables a practice of letting go and trusting in divine flow. **In the Flow** is a calming blend and can be used before prayer or meditation.

BLEND BREAKDOWN

Rosemary opens your mind to a new perspective of your life's circumstances.

Geranium re-establishes trust in humanity, which results in opening your heart to people. Geranium softens the heart. It helps you to trust that what happens is meant to happen. There is a lesson in every occasion.

Pink Wintergreen teaches surrender to God/universe.

Thyme calms the rage and teaches you to radically forgive people.

Juniper Berry releases fears. It especially releases the fear of losing control.

Myrrh grounds the spirit and provides feelings of safety. It is common to feel uneasy during times of change. Myrrh helps you to feel secure and calm, despite changes in routine or environments.

Helichrysum mends the heart. It is often referred to as "liquid stitches." Physically, Helichrysum is excellent at closing a bleeding wound. On the emotional side, it stitches up a bleeding heart. Helichrysum heals your heart and allows you to experience love and trust again.

Indian Sandalwood increases your connection to God/universe. This way you are guided from a divine place to live your highest purpose in every moment.

Ylang Ylang brings you back to your inner child. This inspires you to be in awe of the beauty that surrounds you, just like an innocent child who is mesmerized by simple things. It will become difficult to stay irritated when all you see is abundant beauty.

Blends for Hope

DROPS

8 Geranium

5 Lavender

5 Bergamot

3 Wild Orange

5 Ylang Ylang

2 Helichrysum

3 Tangerine

2 Clary Sage

Place drops in a 5 ml roller bottle. Fill the rest with fractionated coconut oil. Apply to inside of wrists, behind the ears and on the chest.

May Flowers Bloom

May Flowers Bloom is used when you have come through a dark time. This helps the weary soul to see the blossoms of life begin to open and bring hope to the heart. Life is like a pendulum: there are times of difficulty, and times of opportunity.

May Flowers Bloom is an excellent blend to use during the transition time of difficulty to opportunity. You endure only so much hardship before light begins to shine.

BLEND BREAKDOWN

Geranium allows you to trust that goodness is coming.

Lavender helps you to relax and receive the beauty that surrounds you.

Bergamot is a great regenerating oil for times when you are disheartened. It will also change your perception of reality from the "glass half-empty" to the "glass half-full." You will see the magnificence in seemingly simple moments.

Wild Orange amplifies the delightful blossoms you see around you.

Ylang Ylang soothes and heals the heart from betrayal, allowing for openness once again.

Helichrysum removes the pain from traumatic relationships and restores confidence in humanity.

Tangerine allows you to take in the sweet scent of the blossoms.

Clary Sage provides a clear vision of the future, showing you a brighter path.

Out of Darkness is used when you have completely lost hope and faith in a better life. Especially when it feels like the world is against you. This blend will help you see the light at the end of the tunnel, and may give you a deep sense of hope that things are about to turn around and life will be in your favor. If you have a friend or a loved one who has given up and is hiding from the world, bless this person with this blend. Watch his or her demeanor change and their soul light up.

DROPS

- 8 Bergamot
- 5 Ginger
- 8 Lemon
- 3 Peppermint
- 2 Juniper Berry
- 2 Frankincense
- 1 Eucalyptus
- 1 Clary Sage
- 1 Ylang Ylang
- 1 Siberian Fir

Place drops in a 5 ml roller bottle. Fill the rest with fractionated coconut oil. Apply over the heart area, inside of wrists and back of neck. This blend can be applied up to five times per day.

Out of Darkness

BLEND BREAKDOWN

Bergamot brings you out of deep sadness. It is the oil that allows you to see the light at the end of the tunnel.

Ginger encourages you to be an active participant in your life. Ginger creates movement rather than sitting back and letting life pass you by.

Lemon is a cleansing oil. It purifies thoughts that do not contribute to your well-being. Lemon brings clarity so you can see what is truth and what are lies.

Peppermint gets rid of the cobwebs in the head. In Chinese medicine, Peppermint is used to open the mind and move stagnant energy. Its purpose here is to shift the way you view the world, to see hope rather than darkness.

Juniper Berry is an excellent oil for dispelling fears. Whether it's fear of your power, fear of success, fear of failure, fear of rejection, etc. Whenever you are fearful of anything, juniper berry is the essential oil of choice.

Frankincense brings awareness to the lies you've lived by, so that you can release them. Some of these lies include "I'm not good enough," "I'm not smart enough," "I'm a nobody." Frankincense will help you see your beauty and your value to the world.

Eucalyptus will encourage you to reject the idea of giving up and hiding, so you can take seriously your self-care and make the necessary steps toward your healing journey.

Clary Sage provides brighter visions of your self. Clary Sage will also shed light on your highest gifts, as well as your divine purpose. Once those are understood, your desire to live in your divine purpose will increase. It is lack of clarity and not knowing your purpose that can lead to a dark space.

Ylang Ylang helps to connect the mind and the heart, so they are operating as one unit. Western culture tends to live in the mind, and forgets what the heart feels. The connection of the heart with the mind will result in you living in divine flow and operating from heightened intuition.

Siberian Fir inspires you to break free from destructive patterns so that you can live your highest self. Addictions (food, alcohol, drugs, etc.) are a bondage. They have very low vibration and keep individuals in a dark space.

Place drops in a 5 ml roller bottle. Fill the rest with fractionated coconut oil. Apply to the temples and back of neck.

DROPS

8 Arborvitae

5 Black Pepper

3 Coriander

2 Myrrh

1 Wintergreen

2 Thyme

1 Patchouli

1 Lime

3 Grapefruit

2 Cypress

1 Cardamom

Patience

Patience is a great blend for the hotheads! If you get frustrated over the littlest things and have a hard time letting go, this will give you some peace of mind. We can't control every detail in life and expect things to always go exactly the way we want them to. *Patience* will help you to not "sweat the small stuff." Side effects of using Patience include more happiness, radical forgiveness, going with the flow, and enjoying the present moments.

BLEND BREAKDOWN

Arborvitae helps you to feel centered and calm.

Black Pepper uncovers the root of why certain things frustrate you.

Coriander gently helps you to be honest with yourself.

Myrrh brings a sense that everything is going to be ok. It is a nourishing oil that will help you feel safe and secure.

Wintergreen is excellent for the stubborn personality who insists their way is the only way. Wintergreen creates openness to other possibilities.

Thyme creates openness of the heart and dissipates anger.

Patchouli brings you into the present moment and helps you to develop a deeper appreciation of the life you have been given.

Lime is used to quickly circulate the blend throughout the system.

Grapefruit increases respect for the ebb and flow of life.

Cypress creates extreme movement of the spirit and removes stagnation.

Cardamom provides you with a bigger picture to see the purpose in all events that come your way.

Diffuser
Blends

DROPS

1 Ginger

2 Wild Orange

1 Patchouli

Empowered

Diffuse *Empowered* while reading or listening to personal development. This will take your learning deeper and ingrain it into your spirit. Some individuals will read or listen to powerful books, yet fail to apply the concepts into their daily life. Knowledge is not power. It is the application of the knowledge that changes daily habits and changes the trajectory of your journey. We all have good intentions to improve our circumstances. Rather than good advice going into one ear and out the other, diffuse *Empowered* so you begin to apply what you find useful.

BLEND BREAKDOWN

Ginger creates movement, so be prepared to step out and apply what you learn.

Wild Orange instills the belief that you can accomplish your dreams. It looks more than possible; it looks inevitable.

Patchouli takes all that passion and strength and grounds it into your spirit. It is responsible for putting what you learn into physical action. Patchouli is a manifesting oil.

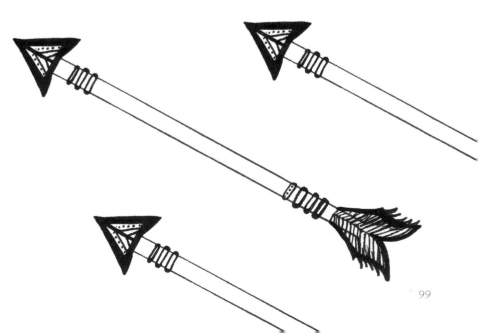

DROPS

1 Cedarwood

1 Lavender

1 Juniper Berry

1 Cypress

Magic

Sometimes we need a little magic in our day. Diffuse **Magic** when you want to feel euphoric and blissful. Don't be surprised if things happen in your favor. You'll begin to see the magic and beauty in the simplest of things. Magic opens your spiritual vision so you can deeply feel people and nature around you. You'll intensely experience the love from close friends and family. After diffusing for one hour, go outside and look at the trees and plants. You may feel their vibrations as well. Magic intensifies the positive vibrations you experience from the world, and mutes any negative vibration. This blend is best diffused during the day. It may keep you awake if diffusing before bedtime.

BLEND BREAKDOWN

Cedarwood helps you to feel the spirit realm, so you can feel divine presence and the angels around you.

Lavender increases your listening skills and the ability to pick up subtle vibrations of people, plants and things. Lavender is the reason why you would intensely feel the love from another person. It magnifies heart-to-heart connection.

Juniper Berry releases any fears associated with feeling good. Some people believe that they don't deserve to feel happy. Juniper Berry allows you to feel good without the guilt.

Cypress moves energy all throughout your body and spirit. It is stagnant energy that blocks you from experiencing the magic that already exists. Cypress creates openness so that you can see the love around you.

*Note: This blend is equivalent to the Fairytale blend in this book.

DROPS

2 Lemongrass

1 Lime

1 Douglas Fir

Clear the Clutter

Do you need motivation to start cleaning up your home? Diffuse **Clear the Clutter** blend and you will get pumped to eliminate all the unnecessary items in your space. In order to create forward movement in your health, career, relationships and even your spiritual life, it is important to purge the excess. The accumulation of stuff we don't need has a tendency to slow down energy and congest our life with toxicity.

I recommend at least once a month that you dedicate four hours of clearing clutter. And now you have this blend to motivate and excite you about the process, rather than feeling overwhelmed and don't know where to begin. I tell people that if they don't know what to do with life and are completely lost, clearing clutter is my first order of business to clear the mind. It opens up the space for new, abundant energy to flow in your spirit. On a deeper note, Clear the Clutter brings feelings of gratitude for what you have, versus feeling like you need more to satisfy the emptiness.

*Note: Be prepared to make many trips to donation centers!

BLEND BREAKDOWN

Lemongrass creates the urge to let go of things we do not need. Lemongrass will also show you that you only need a few things to sustain life. You will begin to see how our Western culture is obsessed with consumption and hoarding.

Lime is responsible for the excitement that overflows your heart for positive change.

Douglas Fir opens the mind so you see your possessions with a different perspective. Your self-worth/value is not attached to things.

DROPS

1 Frankincense

1 Lavender

1 Arborvitae

1 Lime

Calm the Beast

Do you have rage spells when you are screaming at everyone? I'm married with two boys, and I definitely have moments when the anger gets the best of me. It's as if I turn into another person. A raging beast rears its ugly head, and I am not fun to be around.

When you feel the anger welling up, diffuse **Calm the Beast** blend. Immediately it quells the rage and allows you to take a deep breath. This blend has the capability to prevent unnecessary fights and hurt feelings. And yes, ladies, it's even good for the anger/moodiness that comes with monthly cycles.

BLEND BREAKDOWN

Frankincense clears low vibrations—such as anger—from the spirit. It also opens up communication with God/universe so that you can experience more love in your heart.

Lavender soothes the heart and opens constricted energy. Anger is a severe constriction of energy.

Arborvitae brings peace and grounding by helping you "let it go."

Lime brings on the giggles! This oil has a special way of bringing joy to the heart. It helps to free the liver and release the pressure of constricted energy. In Chinese medical theory, the liver organ is associated with anger and frustration. Imagine a pressure cooker releasing steam. Lime releases the pressure built up in the liver, and it will cause you to take a big sigh of relief. Which then leads to a big smile.

DROPS

1 Juniper Berry

1 Cedarwood

1 Wild Orange

1 Lavender

Sleepy Nights

This is an incredibly pleasant-smelling blend. Use Sleepy Nights 30 minutes before bedtime to prepare yourself for a restful sleep. It will calm your mind and put you at ease. This blend is excellent for those who fight going to sleep and desire to stay up all night. Sleepy Nights creates deep relaxation of the body, mind and spirit. It calms your heart and makes you feel like everything is just fine. You'll feel it gradually melt away the stresses of the day.

*Note: If you are a highly sensitive person (meaning sensitive to feeling other people's emotions and sensitive to your environment), then I recommend eliminating Lavender from this blend. About 95 percent of the population does well with Lavender for sleep. But in the remaining 5 percent, Lavender can keep them up at night. If you aren't sure if you are a hypersensitive, then you can test first with Lavender to see if it keeps you up.

BLEND BREAKDOWN

Juniper Berry helps release the fear of listening to your mind. People often watch shows/movies, read books, or work until they fall asleep because they are afraid of listening to themselves. Juniper Berry shows you that your mind is not a dark place; instead, there is light and beauty that resides within. This prepares you for sweet dreaming.

Cedarwood brings comfort in knowing you are loved and protected.

Wild Orange brings pleasant thoughts into your mind before bed.

Lavender settles the spirit so you can relax into a deep sleep.

TESTIMONIALS

"My absolute favorites is *Still My Mind*! As a Wife, Mom, Home school Teacher, Business Owner, and so much more, my mind is always busy. Applying the *Still My Mind* blend is my go to, to help calm all of that mind chatter down. I love to roll it on the inside of my elbow crease, the back of my neck and temples right before I go to bed; so that when my head hits the pillow, my mind can relax. My daughter, (8 years old) also loves to use this blend to help her go to sleep! Thank you Desiree, for this blend and so many more that inspire change and healing in my life!"

Johanna Bradley

"I put *Speak your Truth* on my throat before my counseling appointments and boy do words fly out of my mouth! I also use it when I need to talk and I am nervous, say before class or bringing up a hard topic with my husband. It helps to bring words from my brain to my tongue.

Bye Bye Baggage is also great for decluttering your house, garage and your emotional baggage. You should see the yard sale pile I have and the weight that I have emotionally shed, I feel lighter in my soul."

Amanda Hill

"I have been using the *Manifestor's Blend* for several months and have successfully manifested an array of what I have put my focus on. It has made a huge difference in my life. It has also allowed me to stay within my faith and know that God will provide what I need. It truly has helped me release stress and know that I can manifest my dreams to reality. Thank you so much!"

Kori Abell

"*Still My Mind* helped me when I had jet lag and could not sleep! Applied *Still My Mind* and got great nights sleep. Also sometimes can't go to sleep for hours because of my mind racing. Applied *Still My Mind* and was able to get good night's sleep. Love this blend!"

Wanda Stephens Thomas

"The *More Money* has had a huge impact in my life. I've found that when I use it I find money in random places. Money just kind of shows up! Money that I didn't have in a jacket pocket, or in my wallet. (I Always know exactly how much cash I have, so for money to appear is crazy!) I've found when I use it, I don't stress about money."

Bree Aulph

"My first blend experience was generously given to me by a friend. When my mom passed away from cancer a few months ago, my friend made my dad, sister, and me a roller of *Out of Darkness*. I used it multiple times a day, whenever I felt the flood gates opening or when I just felt despair. I began to find comfort in the scent. Knowing each oil was giving my heart and soul something it needed. The oils and love behind the gift made coping with the loss of my amazing mom a little easier to bear. I was and am able to cope better knowing that she is free and someday I will see here again. The *Out of Darknes*s blend didn't make me numb, it simply provided another source of joy and hope at such a difficult time."

Abby Rose

"*Bye Bye Baggage* has helped me release emotions and things that no longer served my highest good. It also helped me not sweat the small things that really don't matter. It made everything thing so effortless for me, especially letting go of what no longer served me. I am so grateful for this blend along with the work you are doing for this world and humanity."

Paige Worley

"I started with the *Manifester's Blend* to really help me focus and pinpoint my true desires in my personal life and business. I have always had the faith and vision but needed more clarity in the direction I was headed. I use this blend a few times a day by taking a deep breath and visualizing myself both walking my path and at the end my current journey. There is a feeling of encouragement, trust, and an abundance of joy as it truly grounds me into knowing I am doing all the right things and I will succeed."

Sarah Schmidt

CITATIONS

Bensky, D., & Barolet,R. (1990). *Chinese Herbal Medicine: Formulas and Strategies*. Seattle, WA: Eastland Press, Incorporated.

Deadman, P., & Al-Khafaji, M. (1998). *A Manual of Acupuncture*. England: Journal of Chinese Medicine Publications.

(2015). *Emotions and Essential Oils*. (4th Edition). American Fork, UT: Enlighten Alternative Healing.

Kaptchuk, T. (2000). *The Web that Has No Weaver: Understanding Chinese Medicine*. New York, NY: McGraw-Hill.

Maciocia, G. (2015). *The Foundations of Chinese Medicine*. Edinburgh: Elsevier